# Specimen Sight-Reading Tests for Oboe

## Grades 6–8

**ABRSM**

# GRADE 6

© 1996 by The Associated Board of the Royal Schools of Music

AB 2519

**3** Presto

**4** Allegretto grazioso

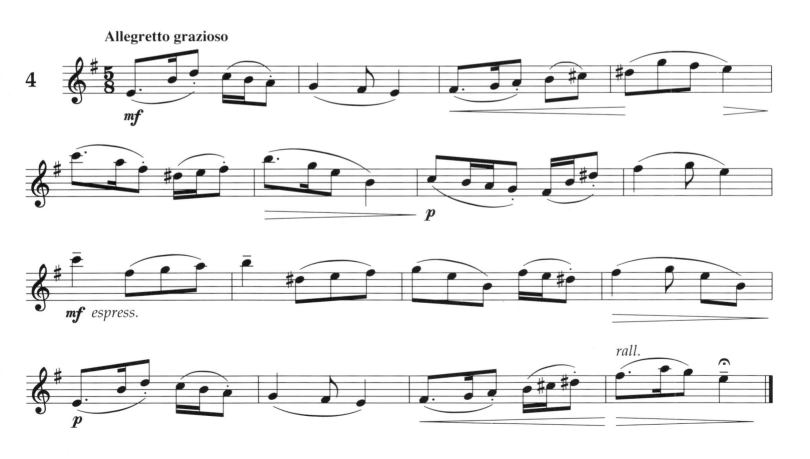

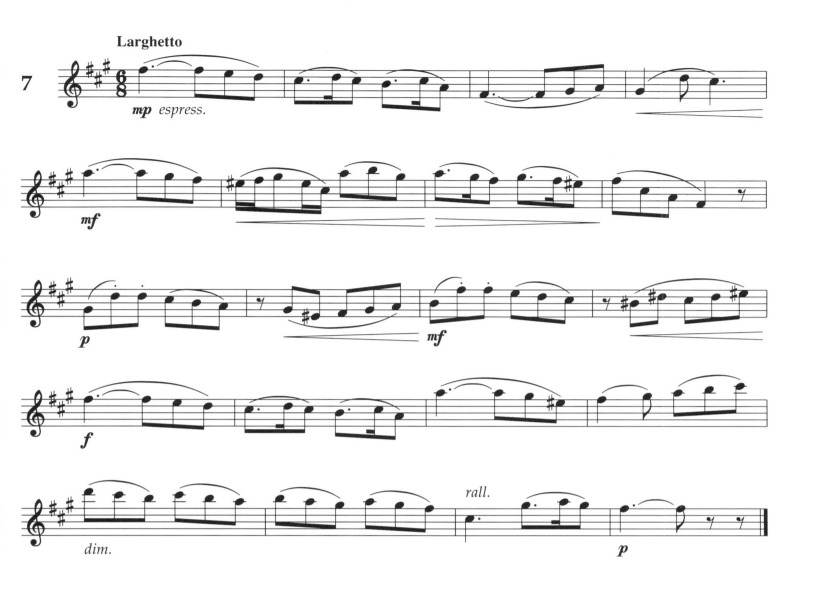

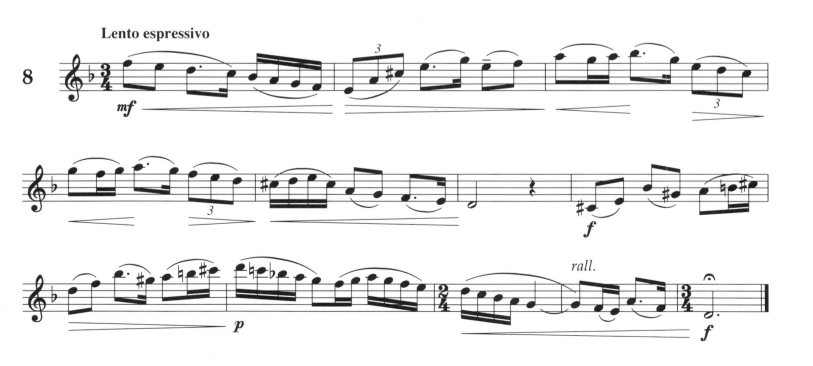

# GRADE 7

# GRADE 8

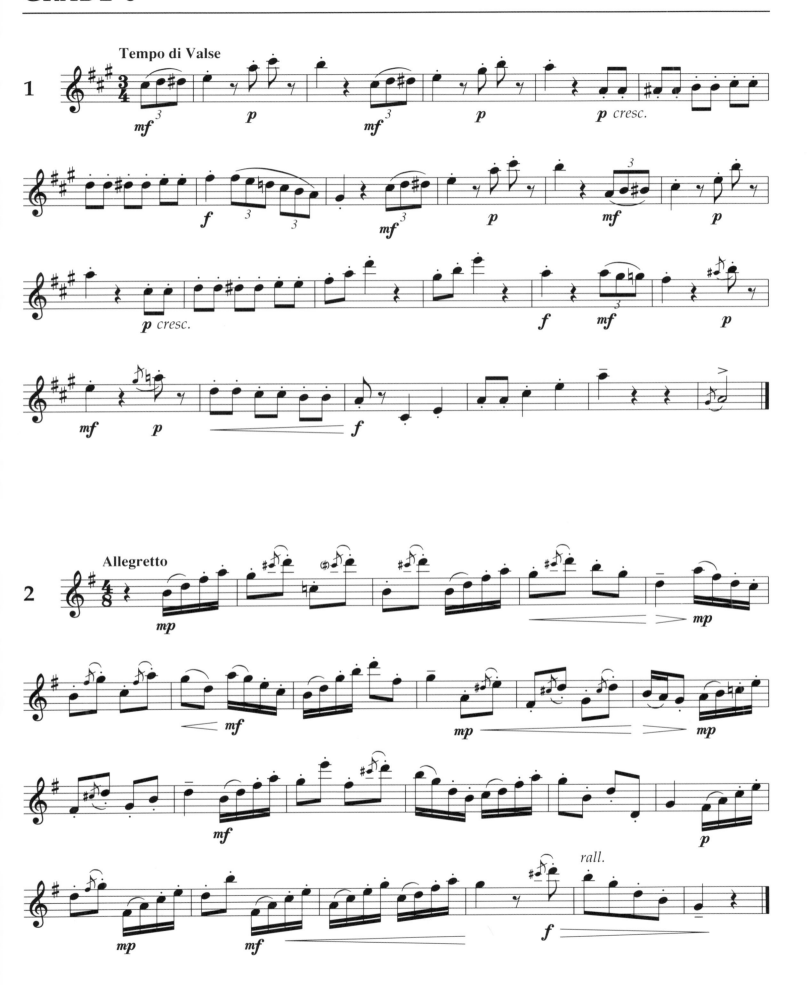

AB 2519    Printed in England by Caligraving Limited Thetford Norfolk    7.11